CRAZY CHRISTMAS

PUZZLE BOOK

Puzzles and pictures by
Steve Weatherill

PICCOLO BOOKS
A Piccolo Original

First published 1989 by Pan Books Ltd,
Cavaye Place, London SW10 9PG

9 8 7 6 5 4 3 2 1

Text and illustrations © Steve Weatherill 1989

ISBN 0 330 31214 6

Printed and bound in Great Britain by
Cox & Wyman Ltd, Reading

It's a dull, drizzly day in deepest December.
The round, rosy robin...

SSSHEESH! ♪♫

Get on with it! WHAT'S THIS?

A PUZZLED READER

O.K. This is Noel Street Junior School.

This is class 3.

This is Trevor.

This is Philip.

This is Hannah.

This is Susan.

This is Roberto.

This is William.

This is Lucy.

....subtract decimal point in the right place right angle with all sides equal to the length of the queue on Friday at the checkout in Tesco roll on 3.30 now long 1066 times by the number of hush puppies in the staffroom coffee machine repeat after me and WRITE out oh no my turn to buy PHILIP STOP THAT rule out subtract and then divide club 18-30 deposit ambre solaire Nigel's birthday ozone layer Fiat Panda 6000 mile service Times educational supplement.....

This is Miss Latimer.

This is Rachel.

...And this is enough of THIS.

You're probably wondering WHY they are all smiling?

NO! I don't think so.

A READER

ARRRGH!

CORRECTION PEN

A READER

YOU MIGHT ASK Why they are all smiling?

OH, all right then. WHY?

A READER

5

Because they're all thinking about...

CHRISTMAS

Oi!

Oh! I nearly forgot little Morgan Thomas. He's not old enough to go to school yet. He's Hannah's brother.

Wanna fight?

WEAK DAZE

Yes, it's nearly Christmas. Philip is feeling WEAK and Susan is in a DAZE.

Can you work out from the picture clues what 6 of these 7 words are?
Then write in the MYSTERY word No.5.

♫♪ I'm dreaming of a **Y Christmas?**

In this picture there are lots of words which end in **Y**.

CAN YOU SPOT THEM?

SUN SPOT

It's only 7 days until Christmas, but where have all the T.V. sets gone?

Here they are sunning themselves on a tropical beach.

Unable to face another festive season, they've taken a last minute winter break to the Gambia.

Here they are again, the next day, but there are **10** DIFFERENCES – CAN YOU SPOT THEM?

MEANWHILE, the kids are visiting Trevor's Granny in a desperate search for a T.V. set.

GRANNY'S I.D. CARD

Trevor has sent his Gran two identical cards. One is for her and one is for her cat Gingey. CAN YOU SEE THEM?

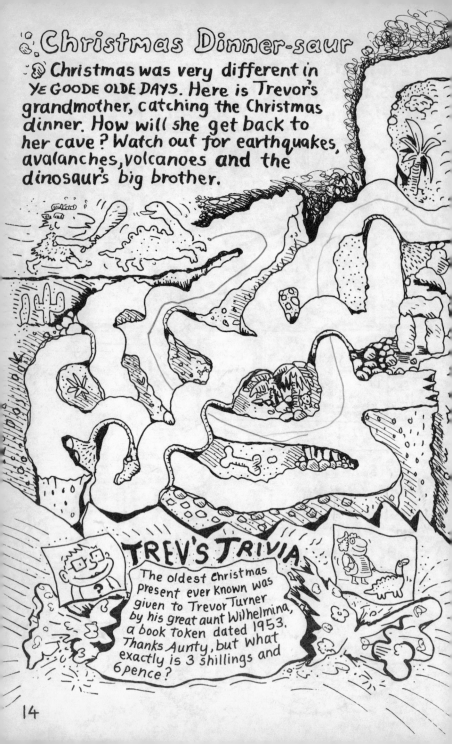

Christmas Dinner-saur

Christmas was very different in YE GOODE OLDE DAYS. Here is Trevor's grandmother, catching the Christmas dinner. How will she get back to her cave? Watch out for earthquakes, avalanches, volcanoes and the dinosaur's big brother.

TREV'S TRIVIA

The oldest Christmas present ever known was given to Trevor Turner by his great aunt Wilhelmina, a book token dated 1953. Thanks Aunty, but what exactly is 3 shillings and 6 pence?

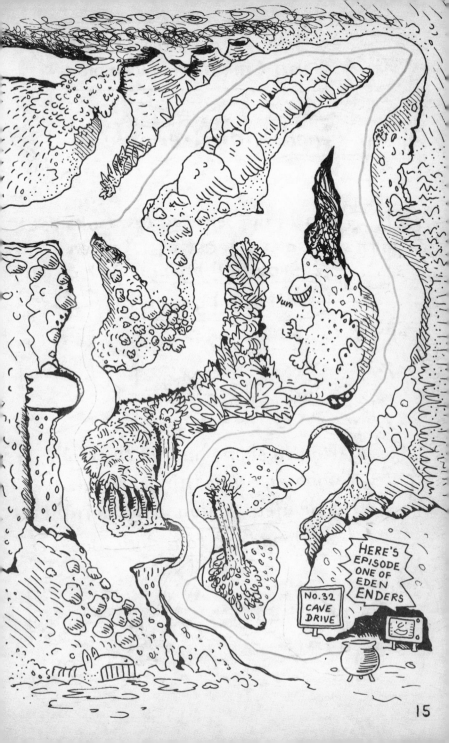

15

Was that **Ye Olde Christmas Carols,** Gran?

While shepherds washed their socks by night,
all hanging on the line.
The Angel of the lord came down
and said, Those socks are mine!

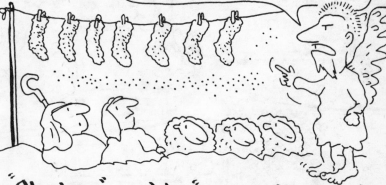

"Oh dear," said he, "my mighty tread has worn these stockings through.
He asked St. Michael for some more.
These holey ones won't do.

The old pantomime...

④

MADE

⑤

SNOGS

Some popular...

And two people to be the pantomime...

A rose by any other name would smell as sweet...

You're in THE WRONG BOOK, MATE!

Ooh err...

⑥

M
+h

ROSE

20

NUMBERSKULL

It's the day of the Christmas panto
and William is making a poster.
He's a WIZ with figures, but can't read
very well. There are 26 letters in the
alphabet, so he's
given each one
a number.

Yup. Now I can remember where each letter should go.

CAN YOU WORK OUT WHAT
HIS POSTER WILL SAY?

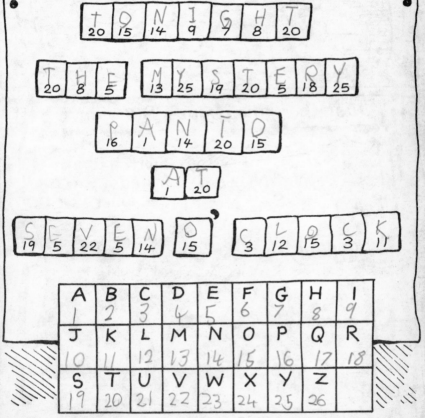

T	O	N	I	G	H	T
20	15	14	9	7	8	20

T	H	E		M	Y	S	T	E	R	Y
20	8	5		13	25	19	20	5	18	25

P	A	N	T	O
16	1	14	20	15

A	T
1	20

S	E	V	E	N		O'		C	L	O	C	K
19	5	22	5	14		15		3	12	15	3	11

A	B	C	D	E	F	G	H	I
1	2	3	4	5	6	7	8	9
J	K	L	M	N	O	P	Q	R
10	11	12	13	14	15	16	17	18
S	T	U	V	W	X	Y	Z	
19	20	21	22	23	24	25	26	

THE MYSTERY PANTO

Scene 1. A lonely wood in the middle of the night.

Just then, they saw a BIG sign.

BUT, before they could stop her, she'd changed the food into a turbo-charged, 16 cylinder, 5,000 horse power ROAD RACER, with electronic chocolate bar unwrapper and JUMBO-size fluffy dice.

ELECTRIC SUN ROOF

Coming soon! SON OF SUN ROOF

MASSIVE BOOT SPACE

BACK SEAT FOLDS OVER TO REVEAL 5-A-SIDE FOOTBALL PITCH

VERY RUDE NODDING GERBIL IN REAR WINDOW.

Q. What's the difference between a LADA and a TIN CAN? A. A tin can hasn't got a fat wally in specs driving it!

FORD LADA FIAT NISSAN AUSTIN

OH, I nearly forgot. You'll need these MAGIC BOOTS.

This is a page from the Hairy Godmother's secret spell book. Look at the PICTURE CLUES, then see if you can write in the 3 magic words which change SHOE to BOOT.

Change one letter at a time.

S H O E

S H O T

S L O T

B L O T

B O O T

Can you change BOOT into GOAL by changing one letter at a time to make 2 new words?

B	O	O	T
B	O	A	T
G	O	A	T
G	O	A	L

GOAL! 41!

BRYLCREAM

CATS

It's nearly MIDNIGHT, Hannah. Time you were in bed! Come home right away.

Mummy.

Hello MOTHER. YES, MOTHER. All right, mother.

Hannah and Morgan just made it home before midnight.

About time!

— Which was LUCKY, because at that moment, the car changed into 2 turkey burgers and 4 of Aunt Suzie's mince pies. So they put them in the dog's dish.

URGH WE CAN'T EAT THAT!

GRRRRRRR

JESS

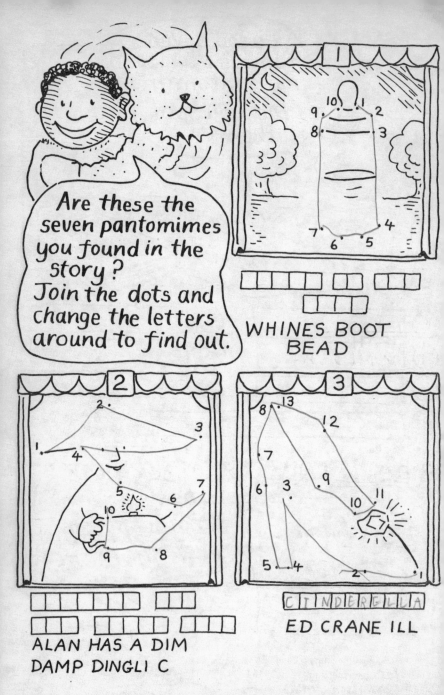

Are these the seven pantomimes you found in the story?
Join the dots and change the letters around to find out.

1

WHINES BOOT BEAD

2

ALAN HAS A DIM DAMP DINGLI C

3

C I N D E R E L L A

ED CRANE ILL

36

CHRISTMAS TREASURE HUNT

Des is selling a trEEmendous lot of trees. How many has he got left?

Fill in the missing letters to complete all the words beginning with DO.

If you wonder what they're looking at down under, then join the dots. Now see how many things in the picture begin with **S**.

15 WORDS IS GOOD.
20 WORDS IS QUITE SPECTACULAR.
1,002934 IS CHEATING!

TREV'S TRIV

Christmas Creek is a small town in Western Australia on the edge of the Great Sandy Desert. December temperatures can reach 100°F, 36°C.
So there's no problem keeping the mince pies warm.

CHRISTMAS CREEK

SYDNEY

MAKE A CAKE

Hannah's mother made a Christmas cake.
Here are 11 of the main ingredients.
Can you find them in the WORD CAKE?

All the words go down or across.

```
C H E R R I E S O O T
U O S I E F L O W E R
R O U C D L F U N I A
R N L E M O N P E E L
A E T G L U E Y R U M
N E A G A R B A G E O
T A N S U G A R T O N
S R A F I L E L E A D
O U S B U T T E R I S
Y O R A N G E P E E L
```

TREV'S MEGA TRIV'

Christmas Island in the South Pacific was discovered by Captain Cook on Christmas Day 1777. He then went on to discover the Sandwich Islands (now Hawaii, 50th state of U.S.A.)

TURKEY AND VEGEMITE SANDWICH CAPTAIN, YOUR FAVOURITE.

ENOUGH TO LAST TILL EASTER ISLAND

CHRISTMAS WAS ABOLISHED by Parliament in England, 1647. Heavy fines were imposed for eating mince pies.

GOTCHA!

In 1660, Christmas was restored.

Worms eat soil for their Christmas dinner. In fact they don't make a big thing out of the holiday at all.

Oh, nothing special. Just a quiet time at home, you know.

Isaac Newton was born on Christmas Day 1642.

BOING

He went on to discover the law of gravity.

Philip's baby brother Luke was born on Boxing Day 1988. He went on to discover the floor and gravy.

The Queen broadcast her first Christmas message from New Zealand in 1953.

RADIO

PICTURE A WORD

Rachel wrote this message and put it up the the chimney. **WHAT DOES IT SAY?**

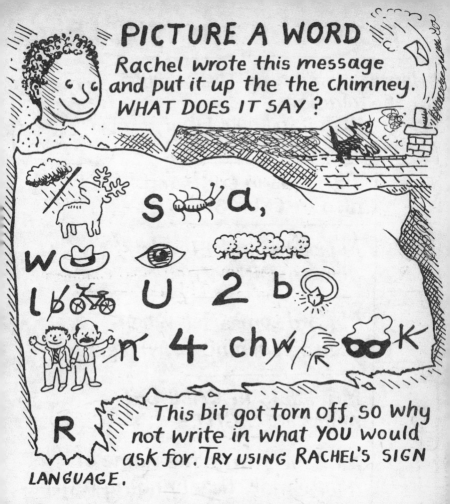

This bit got torn off, so why not write in what YOU would ask for. TRY USING RACHEL'S SIGN LANGUAGE.

RIDDLE IN THE MIDDLE

Here is something thats splits in the middle.
If you want to know what, then solve this riddle!

1 C	My 1st is in CAKE and also in CRUMBS.
2 R	My 2nd is in RED and also in DRUMS.
3	My 3rd comes 1st when you're learning to write.
4 T	My 4th is in CALL but never in SIGHT.
5	My 5th starts the name of a wise man. He's bringing a gift.
6	My 6th is in ELEVATOR, but it's never in LIFT.
7 G	My 7th could be, in RIGHT or in WRONG. But it's not in this line, 'THE END OF THE SONG'.

CHRISMATCH—MISMATCH

WATCH THAT SPACE!

It was the night before Christmas and Roberto was looking out of the window. Was Santa on his way yet? No, not yet, but Roberto saw 4 other things.

WHAT DID HE SEE? Put in the missing letters and find out.

TREV'S TRIV

1968. Borman, Lovell and Anders became the first men to spend Christmas in Space.

APOLLO 8

I saw 3 space ships flying by, go flying by, go flying by...

STAR

Shining brightly in the sky was the Christmas star.

These 10 words also have **star** in them. Can you work out what they are?

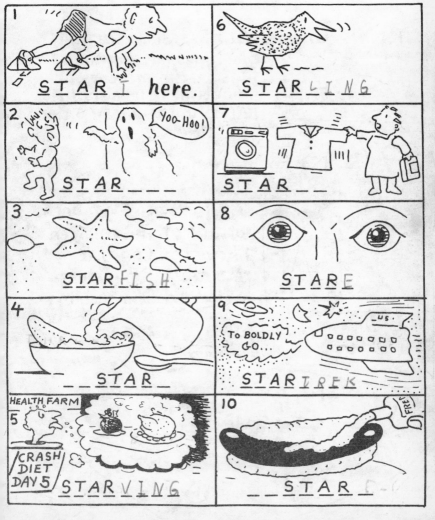

1. S T A R T here.

2. S T A R ___ ___ ___

3. S T A R F I S H

4. ___ ___ S T A R ___

5. S T A R V I N G

6. S T A R L I N G

7. S T A R ___ ___

8. S T A R E

9. S T A R T R E K ___

10. ___ ___ S T A R ___ ___ ___

MISS GNOMER

Deep in the frozen wastes of the silent ARCTIC... But what's that sound?

It's Miss Gnomer, Santa's secretary.
She types out the name tags on the presents, but sometimes she gets the letters in the wrong order.

I'm dreaming of a White Christmas ♪ Just like the ones I used to grow ♪

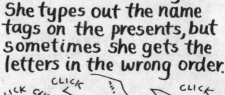

Here are the names of six of the children in class 3. Can you rearrange the letters to find out who they are?

1. NAAHHN
2. CHARLE
3. ROVERT
4. MILWAIL
5. BOOTERR
6. SNAUS

Meanwhile, Rolly the gnome has wrapped up 6 presents.

PICK A GNOME LABELLED ROLLY.

1 DOLL

Rearrange the 23 letters in these 5 words and they will spell the names of 6 presents.

2 LOLLY

3

4

5 BIKE

6 CAR

Got all that? Then decide who should have which present.

GLOBAL MUDDLE TROUBLE

Father Christmas has to deliver presents all over the world. Sometimes the address is hard to work out. Can you tell him WHICH CITIES these parcels should go to?

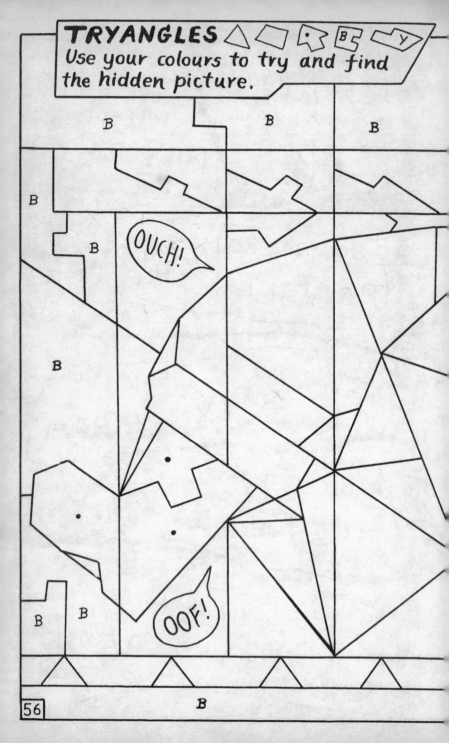

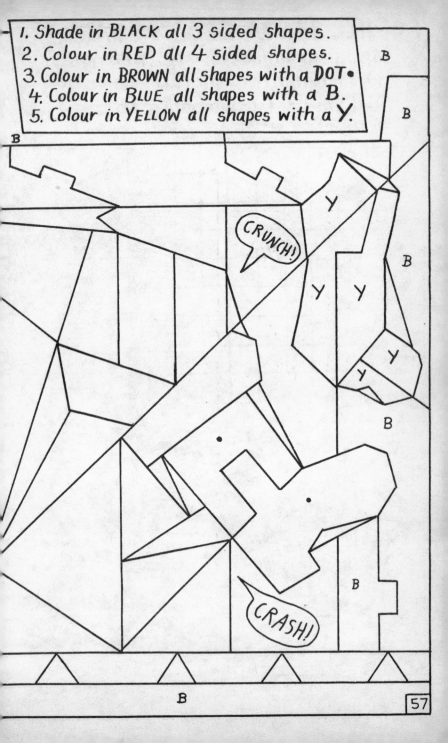

WILL SANTA GET THE SACK?

Fill in the names of the 9 things numbered in this picture. Then you will find out what Santa has forgotten.

1. BOOT
2. CAKE
3. SLEDGE
4. ROOF
5. (blank)
6. SKATES
7. SNOW
8. HOLLY
9. SOCK

THE STOCKING

It's 5.<u>30</u> Christmas morning. The stocking looks **VERY** full.

Using ONLY the letters found in THE STOCKING see how many words you can make. Here are 3 words and some picture clues to get you started.

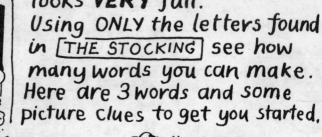

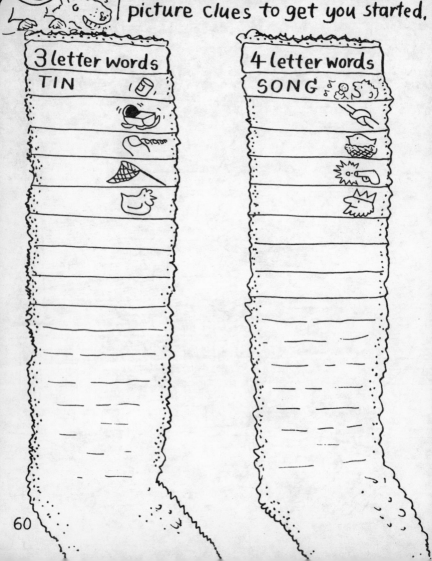

3 letter words

TIN

4 letter words

SONG

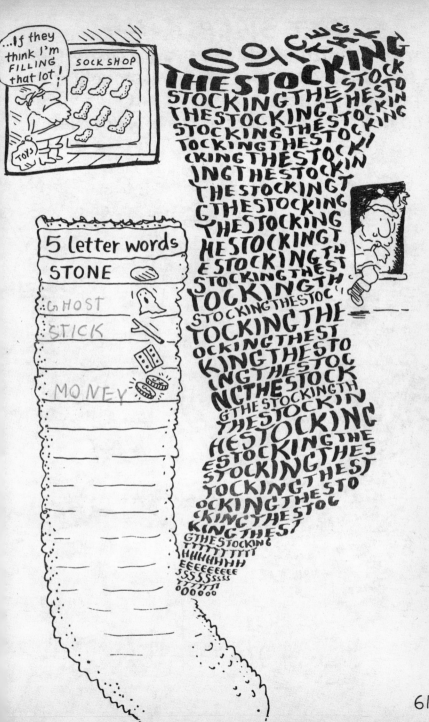

* PET SWAP

All Hannah's relatives have turned up for Christmas and they've brought their pets with them.

Can you tell which pet belongs to which relative?

GILTS DOWN? DOW DOWN?

Grandad Albert

TWEET TWEET

Aunt Deb

Cousin Nigel

G.E. EDITH

Cousin Neville

Uncle Wayne

Auntie Suzie

GNASH

Grandad Albert

sniff sniff

Cousin Tania

PLOP

Uncle Charlie

TREV'S TRIV
Albert Einstein discovered his theory of relativity in 1915. Hannah discovered the dreariness of relatives by December 28th.

Home Movie

Cousin Neville is trying out his new video camera by filming the family party.

Can you match the pictures of Neville filming, with the scenes below from his video?

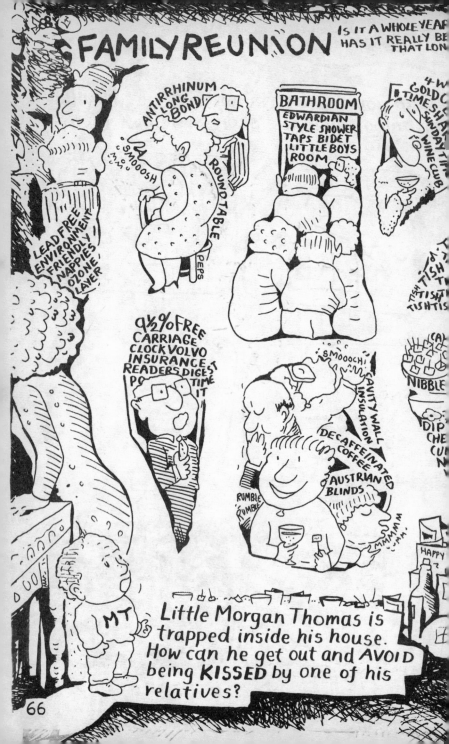

EH! THE OLD FASHIONED NIGHTSHIRTS ARE
YOU DON'T SAY
MARSHALL AND SNELGROVE BEST
CAT LITTER
GARIBALDI BISCUITS
ZAMBUK
HOME AND COLONIAL
12
1926
SMMMM
Come on Morgan!
JACUZZI
RATATOUILLE
SAFARI
LAMBO
DIY NOT CENTRAL HEATING
GERMAN KITCHEN UNITS
U BEND
PASTEL
COPPER PIPE
OLD BRICKS
THATCH
PATIO DOORS
HEY!
TISH TISH TISH TISH TISH TISH TISH TISH TISH TISH TISH TISH TISH
MIDDLE AGE
LOW FAT SPREAD
LEMON
CAMBRIDGE DIET
FIRST PRIZE
MARROWS
CLOCHES
PIGEONS
BRACES
MANURE
CONSERVATORY
TOMATOES
DOUBLE GLAZING
REAL ALE
TUBES
BAVARIAN
PILSNER
OCTOBER FEST
LAGER SPECIFIC GRAVITY
SLOBBER
HAPPY CHRISTMAS
NEW YEAR
CHRIST
MERRY

TOP OF THE GRAND POP'S HEAD

1966. GREEN GREEN GRASS OF HOME. TOM JONES

1967. HELLO GOODBYE. THE BEATLES

1968. LILY THE PINK. SCAFFOLD.

1969. TWO LITTLE BOYS. ROLF HARRIS

1970. I HEAR YOU KNOCKING. DAVE EDMUNDS.

1971. ERNIE, THE FASTEST MILKMAN IN THE WEST. BENNY HILL

1972. LONG HAIRED LOVER FROM LIVERPOOL. LITTLE JIMMY OSMOND

1973. MERRY XMAS EVERYBODY. SLADE

1974. LONELY THIS CHRISTMAS. MUD

1975. BOHEMIAN RHAPSODY QUEEN.

1976. WHEN A CHILD IS BORN. JOHNNY MATHIS.

1977. MULL OF KINTYRE WINGS

Grandpa George is dreaming about the SIXTIES when he still had some hair.
While he's asleep, try joining the freckles on his bald head.

68

1978. MARY'S BOY CHILD. BONEY M 1979. ANOTHER BRICK IN THE WALL. PINK FLOYD

1988. MISTLETOE AND WINE. CLIFF RICHARD

1987. ALWAYS ON MY MIND. PET SHOP BOYS

1986. REET PETITE. JACKIE WILSON

1985. MERRY CHRISTMAS EVERYONE. SHAKIN' STEVENS

1980. THERE'S NO ONE QUITE LIKE GRANDMA. ST. WINIFRED'S SCHOOL CHOIR

1981. DON'T YOU WANT ME. HUMAN LEAGUE

1982. SAVE YOUR LOVE. RENEE AND RENATO

1983. ONLY YOU. FLYING PICKETS

1984 DO THEY KNOW IT'S CHRISTMAS? BAND AID

Draw what you think he looked like miming his BIG HIT on 'Top of the Pops'.

1969

PUDDING ON THE BITZ

OH DEAR, Uncle Wayne ate too much Christmas pudding and while he was asleep, his T-shirt BURST! Don't worry Wayne, we can put it back together.

Match the SHAPE of the bits on the wall to those on Wayne's chest. Then carefully draw in what you see on each piece.

MUM

Q What do they eat for Christmas dinner in Turkey?

A I DONER KNOW.

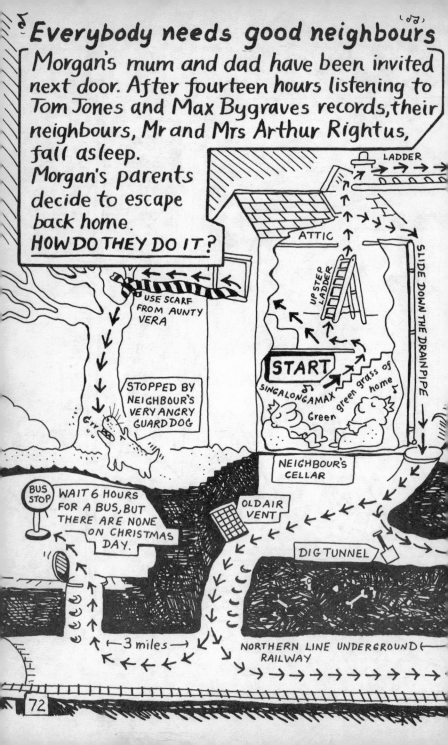

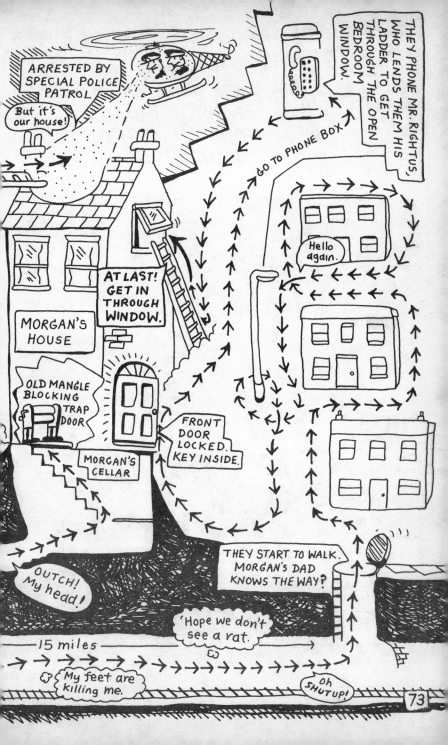

While they wait, they are making New Year's resolutions. Which relative do you think NEEDS to make which resolution?

E I must stop smoking.

F I'm only going to eat curried beans and sprouts every **other** Thursday.

G I won't be recommending my brother-in-law's hair transplant company this year.

77

TWO TRIVS FROM TREV.

FIRST FOOTING

In Scotland, New Year's Eve is called Hogmanay. The first man to set foot in a house after midnight will bring good luck. But he must have dark hair and carry a piece of coal.

LOCH

GOOD-NESS!

Christmas crackers were invented by a London pastry chef called Tom Smith in the 1840s.

Hey, I've got this great idea! I wrap up little gifts in paper, then people pull them apart and they go BANG!

You're CRACKERS!

PATENT OFFICE

So that's why this joke is 150 years old!

ICE AGE, ICE AGE, ICE AGE!

Q What's the difference between a CHOIRBOY and a SNOWMAN?

A One attempts the high notes. The other notes the low temps.

Q What do SNOWMEN use to write their Christmas cards?

A A ballpoint penguin.

A We're flying through the air.

FESTIVE RHYME TIME

LOOK at the picture clues and then work out the missing words which rhyme with

MINCE **PIE**

...and SNOWMAN'S **NOSE**

Look carefully at the pieces of suit and see if you can restore the embarrassed sales executive to his sartorial splendour.

DRAW HIS CLOTHES BACK ON!

ICY MORNING WORDS

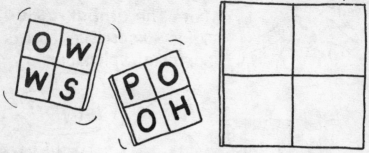

Fit the 4 small squares into the large square so that they spell the same 4 words down and across.

Here is a clue to each word.
Ratty Race, the maths teacher has worked out how wide the school gates are and got it wrong.

A THAWRY THIGHT.

__OH NO!__ A thaw has set in. Everything is melting. Find the 6 magic words which change "SNOW" into "DRIP".

Change only the letter framed ☐ to make the next word.

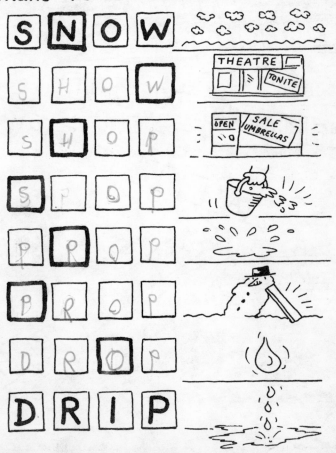

S	N	O	W
S	H	O	W
S	H	O	P
S	T	O	P
P	R	O	P
P	R	O	P
D	R	O	P
D	R	I	P

I bet you can't wait till next Christmas, so here is the whole of next year CUT OUT! Can you put the shredded months back together?

A E A P A U U U E C O E R

Y R B R E E

N B R R Y N L G P T V C

A U H L S E B M M

TREV'S

On the planet Pluto, a year lasts nearly 248 earth years and each day is 6½ earth days long. So Plutonians still have 14,127 whopping days to Christmas!

TRIVIA

85

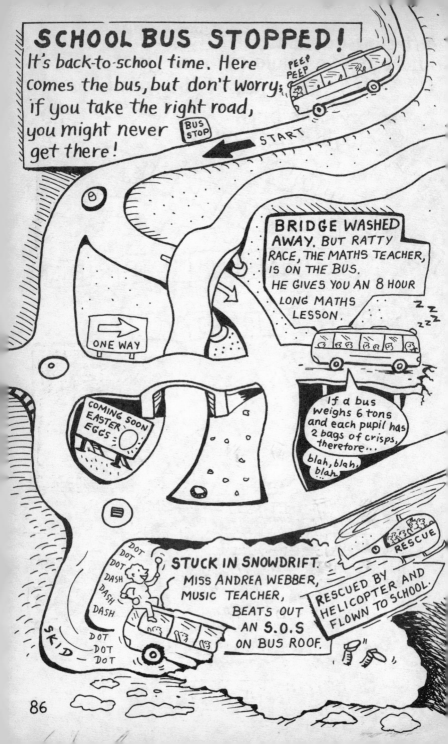

New Year's RESOLUTIONS

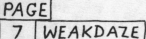

PAGE 7 — WEAKDAZE

① SUNDAY   ⑤ THURSDAY ?
② MONDAY   ⑥ FRIDAY
③ TUESDAY ⑦ SATURDAY
④ WEDNESDAY

I must get it WRITE this year.

8/9 — Y Christmas?

	honey	cherry		jetty
donkey	boy	ivy	strawberry	dinghy
monkey	toy	holly	raspberry	lorry
turkey	key	baby	chimney	teddy
dummy	tray	gravy	money	puppy
jersey	bay	jelly	belfry	

10/11 — SUN SPOT

12/13 — GRANNY'S I.D. CARD

What CAN we NOW?

DING & DONG

MERRILY

88

PAGE

14/15 Christmas
Dinner-saur

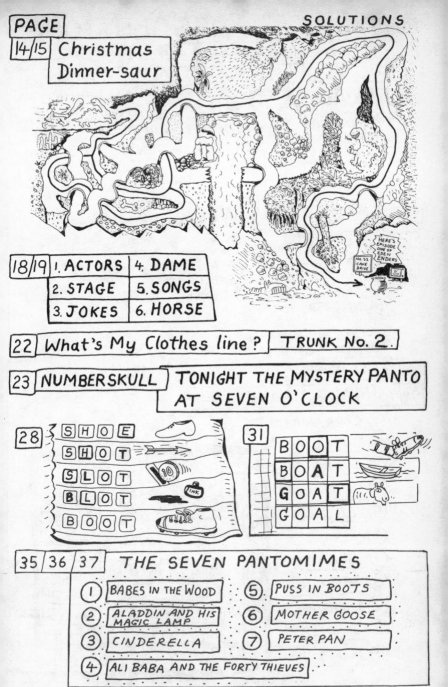

HERE'S
EPISODE
ONE OF
EDEN
ENDERS

NO. 52
CAVE
DRIVE

18/19
1. ACTORS	4. DAME
2. STAGE	5. SONGS
3. JOKES	6. HORSE

22 | What's My Clothes line? | TRUNK No. 2.

23 | NUMBERSKULL | TONIGHT THE MYSTERY PANTO
AT SEVEN O'CLOCK

28
S H O E
S H O T
S L O T
B L O T
B O O T

31
B O O T
B O A T
G O A T
G O A L

35 36 37 | THE SEVEN PANTOMIMES

① BABES IN THE WOOD

② ALADDIN AND HIS MAGIC LAMP

③ CINDERELLA

④ ALI BABA AND THE FORTY THIEVES

⑤ PUSS IN BOOTS

⑥ MOTHER GOOSE

⑦ PETER PAN

PAGE		SOLUTIONS
38/39	CHRISTMAS TREASURE HUNT	42 trees.

40/41 WHAT A TO DO!

1 DOING	4 DONKEY	7 DOUGHNUT	10 DOLL
2 DOG	5 DODGE	8 DON'T	11 DOUBLE
3 DOOR	6 DOWN	9 DOCTOR	12 DOTTED

42/43 SUNNY SIDE UNDER

SANTA   SHIP   SHIRT
SAND   SANDWICH   SKY
SURF   SURFBOARD   SEA
SUN   SUNSHADE   SHELLS
SHARK   SHORTS   STRIPES
STONES   SWIMWEAR   SAIL
SAUCER   SUNGLASSES
SWEETS   SKYSCRAPER
SAUSAGE   SEAGULL

44/45 MAKE A CAKE

1. CURRANTS
2. SULTANAS
3. CHERRIES
4. RUM
5. EGGS
6. FLOUR
7. SUGAR
8. BUTTER
9. LEMON PEEL
10. ORANGE PEEL
11. ALMONDS

C	H	E	R	R	I	E	S	O	O	T
U	O	S	I	E	F	L	O	W	E	R
R	O	U	C	D	L	F	U	N	I	A
R	N	L	E	M	O	N	P	E	E	L
A	E	T	G	L	U	E	Y	R	U	M
N	E	A	G	A	R	B	A	G	E	O
T	A	N	S	U	G	A	R	T	O	N
S	R	A	F	I	L	E	L	E	A	D
O	U	S	B	U	T	T	E	R	I	S
Y	O	R	A	N	G	E	P	E	E	L

PAGE		

47 **PICTURE A WORD** *Dear Santa, what I would like you to bring me for Christmas are...* (eye) (wood)

48 **RIDDLE IN THE MIDDLE** 🦋 C R A C K E R 🦋

49 **CHRISMATCH – MISMATCH**

1	THINK / SINK	2	TREE / THREE	3	CRACKER / QUACKER	4	PRESENT / PHEASANT

5	CAROL / BARREL	6	SWEETS / SEATS	7	SLEDGE / HEDGE	8	ICICLE / BICYCLE

50 51 WATCH THAT SPACE!

STAR ☀:

1	START	6	STARLING
2	STARTLE	7	STARCH
3	STARFISH	8	STARE
4	CUSTARD	9	STARSHIP
5	STARVING	10	MUSTARD

52

NAAHHN / HANNAH	ROVERT / TREVOR	BOOTERR / ROBERTO	CHARLE / RACHEL	MILWAIL / WILLIAM	SNAUS / SUSAN

53 PICK A GNOME LABELLED ROLLY.

1 DOLL

2 LOLLY

3 PEN

GAME 4

5 BIKE

6 CAR

91

PAGE 54 55 GLOBAL MUDDLE TROUBLE

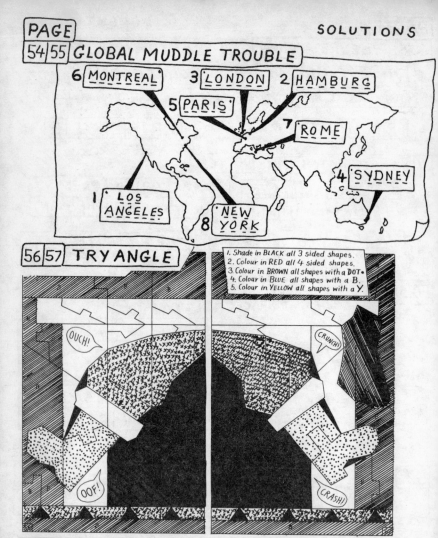

56 57 TRY ANGLE

1. Shade in BLACK all 3 sided shapes.
2. Colour in RED all 4 sided shapes.
3. Colour in BROWN all shapes with a DOT •
4. Colour in BLUE all shapes with a B.
5. Colour in YELLOW all shapes with a Y.

58 59 WILL SANTA GET THE SACK?

1. BOOT
2. CAKE
3. SLEDGE
4. ROOF
5. SNIFF
6. SKATES
7. SNOW
8. HOLLY
9. SOCK

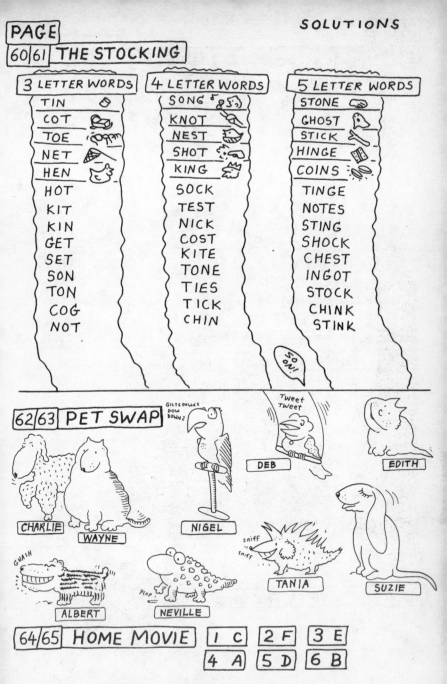

PAGE 60|61 THE STOCKING

3 LETTER WORDS
TIN
COT
TOE
NET
HEN
HOT
KIT
KIN
GET
SET
SON
TON
COG
NOT

4 LETTER WORDS
SONG
KNOT
NEST
SHOT
KING
SOCK
TEST
NICK
COST
KITE
TONE
TIES
TICK
CHIN

5 LETTER WORDS
STONE
GHOST
STICK
HINGE
COINS
TINGE
NOTES
STING
SHOCK
CHEST
INGOT
STOCK
CHINK
STINK

SON!

62|63 PET SWAP

GILTS DOWN 2
DOW DOWN 2

CHARLIE
WAYNE
NIGEL
DEB
EDITH
GNASH
ALBERT
NEVILLE
PLOP
sniff sniff
TANIA
SUZIE
tweet tweet

64|65 HOME MOVIE   1 C   2 F   3 E   4 A   5 D   6 B

FAMILY REUNION

Little Morgan Thomas is trapped inside his house. How can he get out and AVOID being KISSED by one of his relatives?

68 69 TOP OF THE 'GRAND' POPS HEAD

70 71 PUDDING ON THE BITZ

PAGE 72/73 — Everybody needs good neighbours

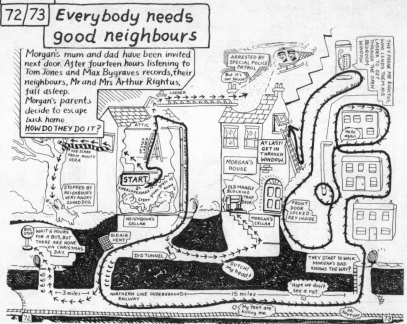

Morgan's mum and dad have been invited next door. After fourteen hours listening to Tom Jones and Max Bygraves records, their neighbours, Mr and Mrs Arthur Rightus, fall asleep.
Morgan's parents decide to escape back home.
HOW DO THEY DO IT?

74/75 WHO'S 'FLU? | 1 LUCY | 2 RACHEL | 3 TREVOR

| 4 ROBERTO | 5 PHILIP | 6 MORGAN | 7 SUSAN | 8 WILLIAM |

76/77 NEW YEAR'S RESOLUTIONS

| 1/C | 2/E | 3/F | 4/G | 5/D | 6/B | 7/A |

---

79 RHYME TIME

PIE — CRY — FLY — EYE — SKY — TIE

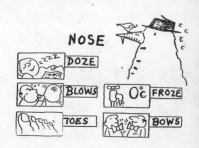

NOSE — DOZE — BLOWS — FROZE — TOES — BOWS

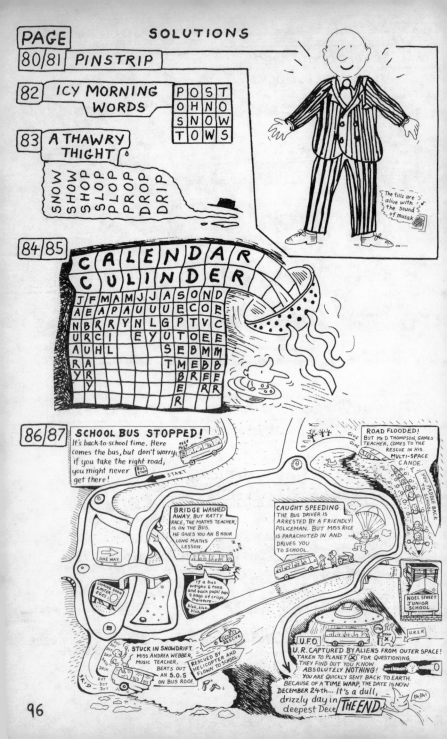